Mental Maths
Practice
4

G000153795

Peter Clarke

Christina Rossiter

Heinemann

Heinemann Educational Publishers
Halley Court, Jordan Hill, Oxford OX2 8EJ
a division of Reed Educational & Professional Publishing Ltd

Oxford Melbourne Auckland
Florence Prague Madrid Athens
Singapore Tokyo Sao Paulo
Chicago Portsmouth NH (USA) Mexico City
Ibadan Gaborone Johannesburg
Kampala Nairobi Kuala Lumpur

First published 1997

00 99
10 9 8 7 6 5 4

ISBN 0435 02411 6
pack of 8: 0435 02416 7
Teacher's book: 0435 02417 5

Designed by Artistix
Typeset and illustrated by TechType, Abingdon, Oxon.
Cover design by Peter Campbell
Printed and bound by Scotprint

Exercise 1

A

1. $29 - 14 =$

2. $10 + 12 =$

3. $1 + 3 + 6 =$

4. $5 \div 5 =$

5. $24 \div 8 =$

6. $1 \times 3 =$

7. $6 \times \boxed{} = 12$

8. $16 - 9 =$

9. $9 + \boxed{} = 13$

10. $0 + 1 =$

11. $2 - 2 =$

12. $57, 58, \boxed{}, 60$

13. $-1 \quad \boxed{} \quad 1 \quad 2 \quad 3$

14. $173, 183, 193, \boxed{}$

15. $35 \times 10 =$

B

1. Add seventeen and twelve.

2. $925, 900, \boxed{}, \boxed{}, 825$

3. What is the value of 7 in 875?

4. $4 + 6 + 5 + 9 + 2 =$

5. 6 multiplied by 3 =

6. How many 5s in 35?

7. What is a quarter of 20?

8. Which 3 coins make 72p?

9. How many faces has a cuboid?

10. I spend 92p. How much change do I get from £1?

11. What is the total cost of a drink costing 35p and crisps costing 25p?

12. I have 49p. I buy sweets costing 38p. How much do I have left?

13. Write the time shown on this clock as a digital time.

14. Round 62 to the nearest 10.

15. $1\,m + 1\,m = \boxed{}\ cm$

How many ways can you make 7, using some or all of these numbers?

$$1 \quad 4 \quad 12 \quad 6 \quad 3 \quad 5$$

(C)

1. $66 - 23 =$

2. $73 + 15 =$

3. $2 + 2 + 9 =$

4. $30 \div 10 =$

5. $24 \div 4 =$

6. $\square \times 6 = 18$

7. $0 \times 10 =$

8. $20 - 10 =$

9. $\square + 6 = 14$

10. $2 + 2 =$

11. $5 - 1 =$

12. 34, 33, 32, $\square$, $\square$

13. $56 \times 10 =$

14. 158, 160, 162, $\square$

15. $\square$ –1   0   1   2

Copy and fill in the missing numbers.

$$
\begin{array}{r}
2\ 3\ 4 \\
+\ \square\ 9 \\
\hline
3\ \square\ 3 \\
\hline
\end{array}
$$

(D)

1. Nineteen minus six =

2. Which of these are even numbers?
   16, 21, 9, 24

3. Write 116 in words.

4. $410 - 4 - 2 =$

5. Which of these numbers is divisible by 2?
   5, 6, 7

6. What are 5 lots of 6?

7. How many halves in a whole?

8. $1\,kg + 500\,g = \square\,g$

9. Sweets cost 2p each. Greg buys 8.
   How much does he spend?

10. Anne has 50p. The drinks are 10p each.
    How many can she buy?

11. What is the remainder if you divide 2 into 9?

12. How many hours between 2·30 pm and
    4·30 pm?

13. $12p + 9p + 7p =$

14. $8\ \square\ 6 = 14$

15. Write 3 in Roman numerals.

Exercise 2

A

1. $28 - 16 =$

2. $21 + 75 =$

3. $3 + 1 + 5 =$

4. $35 \div 7 =$

5. $30 \div \square = 3$

6. $4 \times 10 =$

7. $\square \times 6 = 30$

8. $14 - \square = 7$

9. $9 + 9 =$

10. $\square + 1 = 10$

11. $7 - \square = 1$

12. $67, 68, 69, \square$

13. $95 \times 10 =$

14. $534, 532, \square, 528$

15. $-2 \quad \square \quad 0 \quad 1 \quad 2$

Copy and complete.

×	2	5	4	6
4				
2				
5				
6				

B

1. Add together 25 and 24.

2. $700, 720, 740, \square, \square$

3. What is the value of the 5 in 592?

4. 6 add 3 add 4 add 1 add $7 =$

5. What are 4 lots of 6?

6. How many 3s in 21?

7. Quarter of 24 is $\square$

8. Which 3 coins make 80p?

9. How many right angles has a square?

10. I spend 85p. How much change do I have left from £1?

11. A comic costs 42p and a chocolate bar costs 15p.
    What is the total cost of a comic and a chocolate bar?

12. I have 66p. I spend 54p on cakes. How much do I have left?

13. The time is 6·00. Where would the hands be on a clock?

14. Round 86 to the nearest 10.

15. $1\,m + 25\,cm = \square\ cm$

C

1. $81 - 20 =$

2. $37 + 22 =$

3. $4 + 5 + 1 =$

4. $18 \div 9 =$

5. $18 \div 6 =$

6. $9 \times \square = 45$

7. $2 \times 5 =$

8. $12 - 6 =$

9. $8 + 12 =$

10. $1 + 1 =$

11. $10 - 0 =$

12. 29, $\square$, 27, 26

13. $72 \times 10 =$

14. $-2 \quad \square \quad 0 \quad 1$

15. 571, 671, $\square$, 871

How many 1, 2 or 3-digit numbers can you make using these numerals?

2
5
7

D

1. Seventeen take away six =

2. Which of these are odd numbers?
   18, 7, 41, 6

3. Write 441 in words.

4. $49 - 5 - 3 =$

5. Which of these numbers is divisible by 5?
   10, 11, 12

6. What are 4 lots of 3?

7. How many quarters in a whole?

8. $1\,m + 250\,cm = \square\,cm$

9. Chews are 3p each. If you buy 5, how much will you pay?

10. Arthur has 15p. The cakes are 5p each. How many can he buy?

11. What is the remainder if you divide 3 into 10?

12. How many hours between 6·30 am and 11·30 am?

13. $9p + 13p + 6p =$

14. $18 \; \square \; 6 = 12$

15. Write 5 in Roman numerals.

Exercise 3

A

1 46 − 23 =

2 11 + 46 =

3 1 + 4 + 8 =

4 40 ÷ 4 =

5 28 ÷ 4 =

6 8 × 3 =

7 10 × 1 =

8 ☐ − 4 = 9

9 10 + 2 =

10 2 + 3 =

11 6 − 4 =

12 49, ☐, 51, ☐

13 ─┼──┼──┼──┼──┼─
    −3   −2   ☐   0   1

14 437, 447, 457, ☐

15 26 × 10 =

B

1 What is the sum of 31 and 26?

2 430, 460, 490, ☐, ☐

3 What is the value of the 6 in 361?

4 2 + 6 + 4 + 9 + 2 =

5 7 times 3 =

6 How many 6s in 30?

7 What is a third of 6?

8 1 m + 50 cm = ☐ cm

9 Which 4 coins make 85p?

10 I spend 65p. How much change do I have from £1?

11 I buy felt tips for 55p and a notebook for 20p.
   How much do I spend altogether?

12 Rebecca has 90p. She spends 55p. How much does she have left?

13 Write the time shown on this clock as a digital time.

14 Round 137 to the nearest 10.

15 2 m + 50 cm = ☐ cm

How many squares can you find in this shape?

C

1. $63 - 51 =$

2. $66 + 22 =$

3. $4 + 3 + 4 =$

4. $14 \div 2 =$

5. $18 \div 3 =$

6. $6 \times \square = 48$

7. $\square \times 8 = 80$

8. $20 - 11 =$

9. $6 + 12 =$

10. $7 + \square = 9$

11. $9 - \square = 5$

12. $77, 78, \square, \square$

13. $-3 \quad \square \quad -1 \quad 0 \quad 1$

14. $412, 410, 408, \square$

15. $63 \times 10 =$

How many ways are there of showing $\frac{1}{2}$ this shape?

D

1. Twenty-one minus six

2. Which of these are even numbers? 22, 35, 29, 54?

3. Write 86 in words.

4. $413 - 7 - 2 =$

5. Which of these numbers is divisible by 10? 19, 20, 21

6. What are 5 lots of 7?

7. How many quarters in a half?

8. $1 \text{ litre} + 100 \text{ ml} = \square \text{ ml}$

9. At the fruit shop apples are 10p each. How much will 4 apples cost?

10. The sweets are 2p each. Heather has 10p. How many can she buy?

11. What is the remainder if I divide 5 into 17?

12. How many hours between 10 am and 1 pm?

13. $3p + 5p + 9p =$

14. $17 \square 6 = 23$

15. Write 10 in Roman numerals.

Exercise 4

A

1. $27 - 16 =$

2. $50 + 14 =$

3. $3 + 2 + 4 + 3 =$

4. $25 \div 5 =$

5. $12 \div \boxed{} = 3$

6. $6 \times 2 =$

7. $5 \times 9 =$

8. $15 - \boxed{} = 8$

9. $5 + 8 =$

10. $1 + 2 =$

11. $3 - 1 =$

12. $94, 95, \boxed{}, 97$

13. $254, 354, \boxed{}, 554$

14. $\boxed{} \quad -2 \quad -1 \quad 0 \quad 1$

15. $6 \times 10 =$

B

1. 58 plus 11

2. $520, \boxed{}, 480, \boxed{}$

3. 3 hundreds + 4 tens + 3 units =

4. $5 + 8 + 2 + 1 + 5 =$

5. 4 lots of 8 are

6. How many 6s in 12?

7. What is $\frac{1}{2}$ of 20?

8. How many corners in a hexagon?

9. Which 3 coins make 60p?

10. John spends 55p. How much change does he get from £1?

11. Emma buys an ice-cream for 65p and an apple for 22p.
    How much does she spend altogether?

12. Jo has 95p. She loses 23p.
    How much money does she have left?

13. Which of these clocks shows 2·30?

    a   **b**

14. Round 254 to the nearest 10.

15. $3\,m + 10\,cm = \boxed{}\,cm$

How many ways can you make 12, using some or all of these numbers?

4   1
     3
12
5   2

C

1. $79 - 53 =$

2. $24 + 63 =$

3. $2 + 1 + 9 =$

4. $90 \div \square = 9$

5. $30 \div 6 =$

6. $\square \times 2 = 8$

7. $\square \times 2 = 10$

8. $13 - 6 =$

9. $\square + 9 = 19$

10. $8 + 0 =$

11. $8 - 6 =$

12. 85, $\square$, 83, 82, $\square$

13. 238, 240, 242, $\square$

14. $97 \times 10 =$

15. $-3 \quad -2 \quad -1 \quad \square \quad 1$

D

1. Eighteen subtract eight =

2. Which of these are odd numbers?
   31, 22, 36, 47

3. Write 76 in words.

4. $414 - 6 - 2 =$

5. Which of these numbers is divisible by 2?
   11, 12, 13

6. What is 3 times 6?

7. How many thirds in one whole?

8. $1 \, kg + 200 \, g = \square \, g$

9. Lollies are 5p each. How much
   do 5 lollies cost?

10. Shamilla has 60p. Stickers are 10p each.
    How many stickers can she buy?

11. What is the remainder if I divide 2 into 17?

12. How many hours are there between
    11 am and 7 pm?

13. $8p + 6p + 6p =$

14. $19 \, \square \, 5 = 14$

15. Write 2 in Roman numerals.

Copy and fill in the missing numbers.

$$
\begin{array}{ccc}
 & 4 & 5 & \square \\
+ & & \square & 8 \\
\hline
 & 5 & 0 & 0 \\
\hline
\end{array}
$$

Exercise 5

A

1. $55 - 42 =$

2. $38 + 51 =$

3. $5 + 1 + 3 =$

4. $10 \div 10 =$

5. $24 \div 6 =$

6. $9 \times 3 =$

7. $6 \times 2 =$

8. $11 - \boxed{} = 2$

9. $3 + 9 =$

10. $5 + \boxed{} = 10$

11. $10 - 1 =$

12. $12, 11, \boxed{}, 9, \boxed{}$

13. $10 \times 25 =$

14. $688, \boxed{}, 692, 694$

15. $\boxed{} \quad -2 \quad -1 \quad 0$

Copy and complete.

×	3	2	4	5
6				
5				
8				
7				

B

1. Add 14 and 65.

2. $\boxed{}$, 850, $\boxed{}$, 950

3. 2 hundreds + 6 tens + 3 units =

4. $3 + 4 + 2 + 9 + 8 =$

5. What are 6 lots of 8?

6. What is 16 divided by 4?

7. What is a quarter of 28?

8. How many faces on a cube?

9. Which 4 coins make 90p?

10. Francesca buys a cake for 35p and a drink for 34p.
How much does she spend altogether?

11. Brian buys a bag of apples for 84p.
How much change will he get from £1?

12. Frances has 70p. Her bus fare is 25p.
How much does she have left?

13. Write the time shown on this clock as a digital time.

14. Round 866 to the nearest 10.

15. $4\,m + 75\,cm = \boxed{}\,cm$

C

1. $92 - 81 =$

2. $12 + 43 =$

3. $7 + 2 + 5 + 4 =$

4. $12 \div 2 =$

5. $16 \div \square = 4$

6. $3 \times \square = 15$

7. $2 \times 10 =$

8. $16 - 8 =$

9. $7 + \square = 12$

10. $1 + 3 =$

11. $\square - 3 = 3$

12. $16, 15, \square, \square, 12$

13. $586, 584, 582, \square$

14. $-4 \quad -3 \quad -2 \quad \square \quad 0$

15. $10 \times 11 =$

How many 1, 2 or 3-digit numbers can you make using these numerals?

1 4
3

D

1. What is sixteen take away seven?

2. Which of these are the even numbers?
71, 17, 62, 26

3. Write 212 in words.

4. $416 - 6 - 2 =$

5. Which number is divisible by 5?
13, 14, 15

6. What is 4 multiplied by 4?

7. How many quarters in two wholes?

8. $1 \text{ km} + 100 \text{ m} = \square \text{ m}$

9. It costs 5p to have a go on each game at the school fair.
James plays 6 games. How much does he spend?

10. Harry has 18p. The chocolate mice are 2p each.
How many can he buy?

11. What is the remainder if I divide 10 into 23?

12. How many hours are there between 8 pm and 1 am?

13. $7p + 9p + 4p =$

14. $19 \; \square \; 5 = 24$

15. Write 4 in Roman numerals.

Exercise 6

(A)

1. $26 - 12 =$

2. $86 + 11 =$

3. $8 + 1 + 7 =$

4. $30 \div 6 =$

5. $21 \div 7 =$

6. $6 \times 4 =$

7. $10 \times \boxed{} =$

8. $\boxed{} - 5 = 7$

9. $6 + 14 =$

10. $\boxed{} + 3 = 9$

11. $\boxed{} - 5 = 4$

12. $75, \boxed{}, 77, 78$

13. $\boxed{} \quad -3 \quad -2 \quad -1 \quad 0$

14. $349, \boxed{}, 353, 355$

15. $10 \times 49 =$

(B)

1. What is the sum of 73 and 25?

2. $\boxed{}, 400, \boxed{}, 440$

3. 5 hundreds + 4 units =

4. $9 + 8 + 2 + 6 + 5 =$

5. 6 multiplied by 5 =

6. What is 14 divided by 2?

7. What is $\frac{1}{10}$ of 20?

8. How many sides has a pentagon?

9. Which 4 coins make 75p?

10. Philip spends 87p. How much does he have left from £1?

11. Roberta spends 60p on three pears and then buys a banana for 12p. How much does she spend altogether?

12. Jim spends 55p. He gives the shopkeeper 70p. How much change does he get?

13. Where are the hands on a clock when the time is 3·30?

14. Round 689 to the nearest 10.

15. $2\,m + 3\,m + 50\,cm = \boxed{}\,cm$

How many squares can you find in this shape?

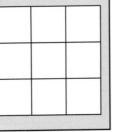

14

C

1. $62 - 41 =$

2. $46 + 23 =$

3. $9 + 9 + 2 + 6 =$

4. $6 \div 3 =$

5. $\boxed{} \div 4 = 5$

6. $\boxed{} \times 4 = 32$

7. $\boxed{} \times 10 = 10$

8. $20 - 20 =$

9. $3 + 10 =$

10. $1 + 4 =$

11. $7 - 2 =$

12. $52, 51, \boxed{}, \boxed{}$

13. $-4 \quad -3 \quad \boxed{} \quad -1 \quad 0$

14. $312, 310, \boxed{}, 306, 304$

15. $10 \times 7 =$

How many ways are there of showing $\frac{1}{5}$ this shape?

D

1. Take five away from seventeen.

2. Which two of these numbers are odd?
   37, 30, 96, 53

3. Write 307 in words.

4. $414 - 2 - 5 =$

5. Which number is divisible by 10?
   28, 29, 30

6. What are 3 lots of ten?

7. How many halves in six wholes?

8. 2 litres + 200 ml = $\boxed{}$ ml

9. The orange drink is 6p a cup.
   Jade buys 3 cups.
   How much does she spend?

10. Steve has 18p. The apples are 6p each.
    How many apples can he buy?

11. What is the remainder if I divide 6 into 13?

12. How many hours are there between
    11 pm and 6 am?

13. $14p + 6p + 5p =$

14. $16 \boxed{} 6 = 10$

15. Write 6 in Roman numerals.

Exercise 7

(A)

1. 68 − 26 =

2. 93 + 6 =

3. 6 + 1 + 8 =

4. 90 ÷ 9 =

5. 8 ÷ 2 =

6. 3 × 4 =

7. 5 × 2 =

8. 13 − 2 =

9. 13 + 7 =

10. 0 + 5 =

11. 10 − 2 =

12. 39, ☐, 41, 42

13. 791, ☐, 787, 785

14. 10 × 19 =

15. −4 −3 −2 −1 ☐

How many ways can you make 10, using some or all of these numbers?

6 1
9
4
2 6

(B)

1. 59 add 20 =

2. 600, ☐, ☐, 675

3. 8 hundreds + 7 tens =

4. 6 + 7 + 3 + 4 + 3 =

5. 10 times 8 =

6. How many 4s in 40?

7. What is $\frac{1}{5}$ of 10?

8. Which 5 coins make 70p?

9. How many right angles in a right-angled triangle?

10. Niyat spends 66p. How much change does he get from £1?

11. Fiona buys a pencil for 25p and a rubber for 20p.
How much does she spend altogether?

12. Jasmine spends 50p. She gives the shopkeeper three 20p coins. What change does she get?

13. Write the time shown on this clock as a digital time.

14. Round 125 to the nearest 100.

15. 3 m + 3 m + 25 cm = ☐ cm

C

1. $72 - 30 =$

2. $13 + 45 =$

3. $5 + 2 + 6 + 9 =$

4. $8 \div 2 =$

5. $60 \div 6 =$

6. $\square \times 6 = 42$

7. $\square \times 10 = 0$

8. $19 - 14 =$

9. $8 + 3 =$

10. $\square + 6 = 6$

11. $\square - 4 = 4$

12. $68, 69, \square, 71$

13. $765, 770, 775, \square$

14. $-5 \quad -4 \quad \square \quad -2 \quad -1$

15. $78 \times 10 =$

Copy and fill in the missing numbers.

$$5 \; \square \; 2$$
$$+ \quad 4 \quad 9$$
$$\overline{\square \quad 2 \quad 1}$$

D

1. Fourteen take away eleven.

2. Which of these numbers are even?
65, 64, 79, 90

3. Write 390 in words.

4. $16 - 6 - 7 =$

5. Which number is divisible by 2?
23, 24, 25

6. What are 5 lots of 9?

7. How many thirds in two wholes?

8. $2 \, \text{km} + 300 \, \text{m} = \square \, \text{m}$

9. The chocolate mice are 2p each. How much do 10 chocolate mice cost?

10. Bananas are on special offer. They cost 4p each.
Tony has 16p. How many can he buy?

11. What is the remainder if I divide 4 into 17?

12. How many hours are between 1 am and 1 pm?

13. $7p + 6p + 9p =$

14. $16 \; \square \; 8 = 24$

15. Write 8 in Roman numerals.

Exercise 8

(A)

1. $25 - 11 =$

2. $84 - 13 =$

3. $4 + 5 + 9 =$

4. $40 \div 5 =$

5. $27 \div 9 =$

6. $1 \times 6 =$

7. $3 \times 5 =$

8. $\square - 5 = 6$

9. $\square + 5 = 14$

10. $1 + 5 =$

11. $9 - 2 =$

12. 24, 23, 22, $\square$, $\square$

13. -5 $\square$ -3 -2 -1

14. 468, $\square$, 472, 474

15. $37 \times 10 =$

Copy and complete.

×	2	10	9	7
1				
6				
0				
3				

(B)

1. What is the total of 63 and 16?

2. $\square$, 280, $\square$, 200

3. 4 hundreds + 6 tens + 9 units =

4. $4 + 2 + 9 + 8 + 6 =$

5. 10 lots of 6 =

6. How many 4s in 36?

7. What is $\frac{1}{5}$ of 50?

8. Which 5 coins make 85p?

9. Susie finds £1. She spends 78p. How much does she have left?

10. What is the total cost of a notebook costing 42p and a pencil costing 18p?

11. Jean has 65p. She spends 52p. How much does she have left?

12. Which clock shows 5·15?

   a   b

13. How many faces has a triangular pyramid?

14. Round 346 to the nearest 100.

15. $1\,m + 5\,m + 40\,cm = \square\ cm$

C

1 86 − 52 =

2 55 − 22 =

3 3 + 3 + 7 + 7 =

4 6 ÷ 2 =

5 40 ÷ ☐ = 10

6 ☐ × 3 = 0

7 ☐ × 9 = 45

8 17 − 4 =

9 5 + 13 =

10 4 + 4 =

11 6 − 1 =

12 46, 47, 48, ☐

13 ☐ −4 −3 −2 −1

14 466, 464, 462, ☐

15 10 × 94 =

How many 1, 2 or 3-digit numbers can you make using these numerals?

8 5 4

D

1 Take six from twenty-two.

2 Which of these numbers are odd?
7, 93, 46, 52

3 Write 651 in words.

4 17 − 6 − 8 =

5 Which number is divisible by 5?
23, 24, 25

6 What is 2 multiplied by 9?

7 How many halves in ten wholes?

8 3 kg + 500 g = ☐ g

9 At the car boot sale all toys are 10p each. Carmen buys 3 toys. How much will she have to pay?

10 Ahmed has 20p. The biscuits are 4p each. How many biscuits can he buy?

11 What is the remainder if I divide 3 into 20?

12 How many hours are there between 8·30 am and 2·30 pm?

13 16p + 7p + 5p =

14 20 ☐ 8 = 12

15 Write 7 in Roman numerals.

Exercise 9

A

1   44 − 23 =

2   34 + 43 =

3   2 + 3 + 8 =

4   20 ÷ 10 =

5   12 ÷ 6 =

6   0 × 4 =

7   10 × 3 =

8   14 − 3 =

9   7 + 12 =

10   7 + ☐ = 7

11   5 − ☐ = 2

12   92, 90, ☐, ☐

13   −5   −4   −3   ☐   −1

14   804, 807, 810, ☐

15   45 × 10 =

B

1   81 plus 14 =

2   830, ☐, 870, ☐

3   5 hundred + 0 tens + 8 units =

4   4 + 9 + 8 + 1 + 7 =

5   4 times 7 =

6   How many 6s in 18?

7   What is $\frac{1}{3}$ of 12?

8   Which 4 coins make 45p?

9   How many sides has an octagon?

10   Charles has £1. He spends 82p.
How much change does he get?

11   If you buy 2 drinks costing 35p each,
how much will you spend?

12   Sarah has four 20p pieces. She spends 70p.
How much money does she have left?

13   Write the time shown on
this clock as a digital
time.

14   Round 875 to the nearest 100.

15   5 m + 4 m + 30 cm = ☐ cm

How many squares can you find in this shape?

C

1 92 − 20 =

2 14 + 72 =

3 7 + 7 + 8 =

4 18 ÷ ☐ = 9

5 15 ÷ ☐ = 3

6 ☐ × 7 = 21

7 ☐ × 7 = 0

8 ☐ − 9 = 11

9 ☐ + 6 = 11

10 6 + 1 =

11 4 − 1 =

12 87, 88, 89, ☐

13 579, ☐, 583, 585

14 −5 −4 −3 −2 ☐

15 10 × 84 =

How many ways are there of showing $\frac{1}{3}$ this shape?

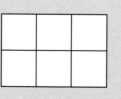

D

1 Twenty-five take away seven.

2 Which of these numbers are even?
16, 95, 43, 58

3 Write 505 in words.

4 418 − 7 − 10 =

5 Which of these numbers is divisible by 10?
49, 50, 51

6 What are 6 lots of 7?

7 How many quarters in 3 wholes?

8 4 l + 500 ml = ☐ ml

9 Bananas are 4p each. Mary buys a bunch of 3.
How much will the bunch cost?

10 Lollies are 3p each. Janet has 21p.
How many can she buy?

11 What is the remainder if you divide 4 into
25?

12 How many hours are there between
9·30 am and 11 am?

13 16p + 9p + 8p =

14 25 ☐ 6 = 31

15 Write 15 in Roman numerals.

Exercise 10

A

1. $24 - 12 =$

2. $52 + 34 =$

3. $8 + 8 + 3 + 2 =$

4. $45 \div 9 =$

5. $42 \div 6 =$

6. $6 \times 0 =$

7. $7 \times 2 =$

8. $15 - 11 =$

9. $1 + 10 =$

10. $10 + 0 =$

11. $10 - 3 =$

12. 50, ☐, 48, 47

13. ☐ 0 1 2 3

14. 936, 934, ☐, 930

15. $58 \times 10 =$

How many ways can you make 8, using some or all of these numbers?

2 3 0 7 4 3

B

1. What is the sum of forty-six and thirteen?

2. 510, ☐, 570, ☐

3. 8 hundreds + 3 tens + 6 units =

4. $9 + 5 + 2 + 6 + 9 =$

5. 4 times 8 =

6. What is 35 divided by 5?

7. What is $\frac{1}{5}$ of 20?

8. Which 5 coins make 90p?

9. How many sides has a rectangle?

10. Jackie spends 76p. How much change does she get from £1?

11. A pen costs 26p and a ruler costs 42p. What is the total cost of a pen and a ruler?

12. How much do I have left from 70p, if I spend 35p?

13. Where would the hands be on a clock at 8·15?

14. Round 762 to the nearest 100.

15. $3\,m + 2\,m + 70\,cm =$ ☐ cm

C

1. $78 - 53 =$

2. $57 + 21 =$

3. $5 + 9 + 4 =$

4. $8 \div \square = 4$

5. $\square \div 3 = 5$

6. $6 \times \square = 60$

7. $\square \times 6 = 60$

8. $16 - 6 =$

9. $7 + \square = 16$

10. $9 + \square = 9$

11. $8 - \square = 7$

12. 35, 34, $\square$, $\square$

13. 432, 442, 452, $\square$

14. $-2 \quad \square \quad 0 \quad 1 \quad 2$

15. $10 \times 23 =$

Copy and fill in the missing numbers.

$$\begin{array}{r} 6\ 7\ \square \\ -\quad 4\ 2 \\ \hline 6\ \square\ 7 \\ \hline \end{array}$$

D

1. Subtract nine from twenty-seven.

2. Which of these numbers are odd?
   21, 32, 43, 54

3. Write 209 in words.

4. $420 - 7 - 6 =$

5. Which of these numbers is divisible by 5?
   39, 40, 41

6. What is 3 multiplied by seven?

7. How many thirds in 3 wholes?

8. $5\,m + 200\,cm = \square\ cm$

9. At the café, Rod buys 3 biscuits.
   The biscuits are 3p each.
   How much must he pay?

10. Laura has 30p. The pencils are 10p each.
    She buys 3.
    How much change will she get?

11. What is the remainder if you divide 4 into 29?

12. How long is it between 9·15 pm and 10·45 pm?

13. $16p + 8p + 12p =$

14. $27\ \square\ 6 = 21$

15. Write 10 in Roman numerals.

Exercise 11

A

1 $23 - 12 =$

2 $15 + 32 =$

3 $5 + 4 + 2 + 1 =$

4 $16 \div 2 =$

5 $12 \div \square = 4$

6 $\square \times 8 = 24$

7 $6 \times 5 =$

8 $19 - 11 =$

9 $\square + 9 = 12$

10 $4 + \square = 6$

11 $7 - \square = 0$

12 251, 253, 255, $\square$

13 $-3 \quad -2 \quad \square \quad 0 \quad 1$

14 137, 140, 143, $\square$

15 $34 \times 10 =$

Copy and complete.

×	6	8	0	4
5				
3				
7				
4				

B

1 Fifteen plus nine.

2 365, 370, $\square$, 380

3 4 tens + 3 units + 2 hundreds =

4 Put these numbers in order, smallest first.
568, 421, 309

5 53 children went on a school trip to the zoo.
Six adults went with them.
How many people went to the zoo altogether?

6 48 pencils have to be put into boxes of 6.
How many boxes be needed?

7 $\frac{1}{2} + \frac{1}{2} =$

8 Sam drinks 200 ml from a litre carton.
How much is left?

9 Which three coins make 75p?

10 How much change from £1 does Jamie get if he spends 83p?

11 How many corners has an octagon?

12 Write the time shown on this clock as a digital time.

13 $(2 \times 6) + 4 =$

14 $1.1 \, m + 3.2 \, m = \square \, m$

15 What is 15 less than 27?

C

1. $47 - 34 =$

2. $72 + 16 =$

3. $3 + 4 + 1 + 9 =$

4. $70 \div 10 =$

5. $32 \div 8 =$

6. $4 \times 4 =$

7. $\square \times 5 = 15$

8. $12 - \square = 5$

9. $9 + 8 =$

10. $2 + 0 =$

11. $9 - 0 =$

12. 349, 350, 351, $\boxed{}$

13. 264, 267, $\boxed{}$, 273

14. $10 \times 57 =$

15. $\boxed{}$ –2   –1   0   1

How many 1, 2 or 3-digit numbers can you make using these numerals?

9
6
2

D

1. Sixteen minus eight.

2. Is 802 odd or even?

3. Write three hundred and sixty-five in numerals.

4. Which of these numbers is divisible by 3? 12, 13, 14

5. Joe planted 29 bulbs. 17 grew into flowers. How many bulbs did not flower?

6. If there are four cartons of eggs with 6 eggs in each, how many eggs are there altogether?

7. Double 22.

8. What is 1 less than 365?

9. Ellen had 35p. Her aunt gave her 15p more. How much did she have altogether?

10. Estimate the answer to $29 + 29$.

11. Complete this pattern. 9, $\square$, 15, $\square$

12. A comic costs 35p. Ian gives the shopkeeper 40p. How much change does he get?

13. What is 16 more than 42?

14. Draw a face that is symmetrical. Show the line of symmetry.

15. What is $\frac{1}{2}$ of 1 m?

Exercise 12

A

1. $73 - 52 =$

2. $26 + 43 =$

3. $1 + 7 + 6 + 2 =$

4. $10 \div 5 =$

5. $42 \div 7 =$

6. $\square \times 2 = 12$

7. $6 \times 10 =$

8. $16 - 10 =$

9. $7 + 4 =$

10. $3 + 3 =$

11. $6 - 5 =$

12. 173, 174, 175, $\square$

13. 543, 443, 343, $\square$

14. $10 \times 92 =$

15. $-4 \quad \square \quad -2 \quad -1 \quad 0$

B

1. Twelve add six.

2. 482, 485, 488, $\square$

3. 1 unit + 3 hundreds + 6 tens =

4. Put these numbers in order, smallest first.
468, 486, 418

5. John's dad gave him 41 sweets and his mum gave him 8 more.
How many sweets did he have altogether?

6. Lollies come in packets of 4.
How many packets will you need to buy to get 24 lollies?

7. $\frac{1}{4} + \frac{1}{4} =$

8. Joanne cuts 25 cm from a metre ribbon.
How much is left?

9. Which 4 coins make 67p?

10. How much change will I get from £1 if I spend 72p?

11. How many surfaces has a cylinder?

12. The time is 6·45. Draw a simple clock face to show this time.

13. $(3 \times 8) + 2 =$

14. $1.3\,\text{m} + 2.6\,\text{m} = \square\,\text{m}$

15. What is 17 less than 29?

How many squares can you find in this shape?

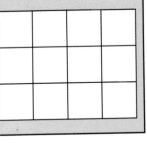

26

C

1. $22 - 11 =$

2. $53 + 26 =$

3. $4 + 1 + 3 =$

4. $50 \div 5 =$

5. $4 \div 4 =$

6. $3 \times 6 =$

7. $2 \times 4 =$

8. $20 - 13 =$

9. $11 + 6 =$

10. $7 + \boxed{} = 10$

11. $10 - 4 =$

12. 437, 435, 433, $\boxed{}$

13. 658, $\boxed{}$, 662, 664

14. $\boxed{}$ −3   −2   −1   0

15. $71 \times 10 =$

How many ways are there of showing $\frac{1}{4}$ this shape?

D

1. Nineteen minus seven.

2. Is 703 odd or even?

3. Write two hundred and ninety-seven in numerals.

4. Which of these numbers is divisible by 4? 15, 16, 17

5. Heather had 17 glasses on a tray. She dropped the tray. She was left with 11 glasses. How many did she break?

6. Six children sit at a table. How many children sit at 7 tables?

7. Double 31.

8. What is 1 less than 2950?

9. Patrick bought a bag of crisps for 23p and a drink for 25p. How much did he spend?

10. Estimate the answer to $58 + 58$.

11. Complete this pattern. 12, $\boxed{}$, 16, $\boxed{}$, 20

12. Franco bought a birthday card costing 38p. He paid with a 50p piece. How much change does he get?

13. What is 18 more than 41?

14. Draw a capital letter that is symmetrical. Show the line of symmetry.

15. What is $\frac{1}{3}$ of 6 m?

Exercise 13

A

1. $8 + \boxed{} = 10$

2. $6 + 8 =$

3. $954, 854, \boxed{}, 654$

4. $\boxed{} \times 4 = 12$

5. $20 \div 4 =$

6. $65 - 23 =$

7. $16 + 31 =$

8. $2 + 5 + 7 + 3 =$

9. $5 \times 10 =$

10. $8 - \boxed{} = 1$

11. $13 - \boxed{} = 8$

12. $48 \div \boxed{} = 6$

13. $473, \boxed{}, 467, 464$

14. $24 \times 10 =$

15.
```
 ┼    ┼    ┼    ┼    ┼
−4   −3   −2   −1   □
```

How many ways can you make 26, using some or all of these numbers?

```
      8
12
         10
    6
 9     4
```

B

1. What is twelve, three and nine altogether?

2. $265, 271, 277, \boxed{}$

3. 6 hundreds + 3 units + 7 tens =

4. Put these numbers in order, smallest first.
371, 317, 373

5. 82 people were queuing for a concert.
Six more people joined the queue.
How many people were in the queue altogether?

6. There are thirty-six flowers. How many bunches of 6 flowers can you make?

7. $\frac{1}{2} + \frac{1}{4} =$

8. Ali cut 250 g from a block of chocolate weighing 1 kg.
How much chocolate is left?

9. Which 3 coins make 72p?

10. How much change will I get from £1 if I spend 69p?

11. How many edges has a triangle?

12. Write the time shown on this clock as a digital time.

13. $(5 \times 6) + 5 = 35$

14. $2.6 \, kg + 2.1 \, kg =$

15. What is 20 less than 59?

28

(C)

1. $7 + 1 =$

2. $5 + 10 =$

3. 631, 633, 635, ☐

4. $6 \times 6 =$

5. $60 \div 10 =$

6. $58 - 26 =$

7. $74 + 15 =$

8. $5 + 8 + 2 =$

9. ☐ $\times 5 = 20$

10. $9 - 6 =$

11. $11 - 10 =$

12. $12 \div 3 =$

13. −5 ☐ −3 −2 −1

14. 349, 351, ☐, 355

15. $10 \times 64 =$

Copy and fill in the missing numbers.

```
  3  6 ☐
 − ☐  1
 ———————
  2  8  1
```

(D)

1. Fifteen minus nine.

2. Is 279 odd or even?

3. Write four hundred and seventy-two in numerals.

4. Which of these numbers is divisible by 3? 23, 24, 25

5. Tom had 26 sweets. He ate 12. How many did he have left?

6. A table has 4 legs. There are 8 tables in a room. How many legs are there altogether?

7. Double 42.

8. What is 1 less than 2792?

9. A rose costs 45p. How much will two roses cost?

10. Estimate the answer to $49 + 49$.

11. Gary got 80p pocket money. He saved 50p. How much had he left to spend?

12. Complete this pattern. 25, ☐, ☐, 40

13. What is 12 more than 54?

14. Draw a symmetrical flower. Show the line of symmetry.

15. $\frac{1}{4}$ of 4 m =

Exercise 14

(A)

1. $5 + \square = 7$

2. $\square + 6 = 13$

3. 821, 820, $\square$, 818

4. $\square \times 3 = 3$

5. $35 \div \square = 5$

6. $67 - 42 =$

7. $27 + 31 =$

8. $3 + 5 + 4 + 4 =$

9. $3 \times \square = 30$

10. $7 - \square = 2$

11. $\square - 4 = 8$

12. $54 \div 6 =$

13. 295, 300, 305, $\square$

14. $-5 \quad -4 \quad -3 \quad \square \quad -1$

15. $10 \times 42 =$

Copy and complete.

×	2	4	9	3
6				
2				
5				
1				

(B)

1. What is the sum of five and twenty-nine?

2. 248, 254, 260, $\square$

3. 4 units + 3 tens + 1 hundred =

4. Put these numbers in order, smallest first.
589, 598, 590

5. James has a collection of 30 toy cars. He got 7 more for his birthday.
How many has he now?

6. How many sets of 4 batteries can be made from 28 batteries?

7. $\frac{1}{3} + \frac{1}{3} =$

8. Penny pours 350 ml from a litre carton of milk. How much milk is left?

9. Which 4 coins make 82p?

10. How much change do I get from £1 if I spend 78p?

11. How many right angles has a rectangle?

12. Which clock shows the time 1·15?

a   b

13. $(7 \times 4) + 3 =$

14. $3\cdot6\,m + 5\cdot2\,m = \square\,m$

15. What is 22 less than 35?

C

1 $2 + 4 =$

2 $9 + 6 =$

3 764, ☐, 762, 761

4 $4 \times 9 =$

5 $15 \div 5 =$

6 $39 - 18 =$

7 $65 + 23 =$

8 $7 + 5 + 1 =$

9 $10 \times 5 =$

10 $1 - 1 =$

11 $20 - 14 =$

12 $8 \div$ ☐ $= 2$

13 ☐ −1 0 1 2

14 791, 789, 787, ☐

15 $9 \times 10 =$

How many 1, 2 or 3-digit numbers can you make using these numerals?

3
4
7

D

1 Twenty-one minus seven.

2 Is 284 odd or even?

3 Write one hundred and eighty-six in numerals.

4 Which of these numbers can be divided by 6?
17, 18, 19

5 Irene collected 57 shells on the beach. When she got home she discovered that she had only 36 in the bag. How many had she lost?

6 There are 10 pencils in a packet. How many pencils are there in 9 packets?

7 Double 21.

8 What is 1 less than 2465?

9 Sita saved 25p from her pocket money. Last week she had saved 33p. How much has she saved in two weeks?

10 Estimate the answer to $48 + 48$.

11 Angie had 60p. She spent 52p on a magazine. How much had she left?

12 Complete this pattern.
18, ☐, ☐, 27

13 What is 12 more than 75?

14 Draw a symmetrical house. Show the line of symmetry.

15 $\frac{1}{2}$ of 6 m =

Exercise 15

A

1. $0 + 4 =$

2. $5 + 7 =$

3. $551, 541, 531, \boxed{}$

4. $\boxed{} \times 1 = 6$

5. $30 \div 3 =$

6. $98 - 36 =$

7. $63 + 12 =$

8. $4 + 6 + 5 + 6 =$

9. $\boxed{} \times 2 = 20$

10. $10 - 5 =$

11. $13 - \boxed{} = 6$

12. $36 \div 4 =$

13. $-2 \quad -1 \quad \boxed{} \quad 1 \quad 2$

14. $\boxed{}, 669, 667, 665$

15. $10 \times 13 =$

B

1. Total eight and thirty-six.

2. $592, 600, 608, \boxed{}$

3. 2 hundreds + 0 units + 3 tens =

4. Put these numbers in order, smallest first.
878, 887, 807

5. Twenty-four birds are sitting on a wire.
5 more join them.
How many birds are there altogether?

6. How many groups of 3 children can you get from 27 children?

7. $\frac{1}{4} + \frac{1}{4} + \frac{1}{4} =$

8. Jude cuts 40 cm from a metre of string.
How much string is left?

9. Which 5 coins make 55p?

10. How much change is there from £1 after spending 52p?

11. How many surfaces has a cube?

12. Write the time shown on this clock as a digital time.

13. $(6 \times 9) + 2 =$

14. 3·4 litres + 2·5 litres =

15. What is 23 less than 49?

How many triangles can you find in this shape?

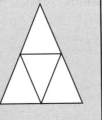

C

1   $0 + 9 =$

2   $4 + 8 =$

3   273, ☐, 271, 270

4   $2 \times 3 =$

5   $15 \div 3 =$

6   $53 - 22 =$

7   $17 + 31 =$

8   $7 + 4 + 7 + 8 =$

9   $2 \times 0 =$

10 ☐ $- 5 = 3$

11 $11 - 8 =$

12 $30 \div$ ☐ $= 10$

13 425, 435, 445, ☐

14 ─┬───┬──┬──┬─
    −3   ☐ −1 0 1

15 $10 \times 74 =$

D

1   What is thirteen minus eight?

2   Is 373 odd or even?

3   Write eight hundred and seven in numerals.

4   Which of these numbers is divisible by 4? 26, 27, 28

5   There were 23 swans on a lake. 11 swam away. How many swans were left?

6   Stamps come in books of 4. How many stamps will I have if I buy 9 books?

7   Double 15.

8   What is 1 less than 6666?

9   At the school fair, Lucy bought a raffle ticket for 15p and a cake for 17p. How much did she spend?

10 Estimate the answer to $79 + 79$.

11 Giovanni had 92p. He spent 50p at the car boot sale. How much did he have left?

12 Complete this pattern. 18, ☐, ☐, 36

13 What is 11 more than 84?

14 Draw a symmetrical candle. Show the line of symmetry.

15 $\frac{1}{5}$ of $10\,\text{m} =$

How many ways are there of showing $\frac{1}{2}$ this shape?

Exercise 16

(A)

1. $4 + 3 =$

2. $6 + 5 =$

3. 354, 344, 334, ☐

4. $4 \times 6 =$

5. $14 \div 7 =$

6. $88 - 61 =$

7. $64 + 25 =$

8. $1 + 8 + 9 =$

9. $5 \times \boxed{} =$

10. $9 - 7 =$

11. $19 - 12 =$

12. $54 \div 9 =$

13. ─┼─────┼─────┼─────┼─────┼─
    −3   −2   −1   ☐   1

14. 350, 400, 450, ☐

15. $10 \times 93 =$

(B)

1. What is four add twelve?

2. 986, 979, 972, ☐

3. 5 units + 4 hundreds + 0 tens =

4. Put these numbers in order, smallest first.
   616, 606, 661

5. There are seventy-nine people at the cinema. Eleven people come in late. How many people watch the film altogether?

6. How many boxes of 6 eggs can you fill from 24 eggs?

7. $\frac{1}{5} + \frac{1}{5} =$

8. Sylvia cuts 150 g from a 1 kg block of cheese. How much is left?

9. Which 4 coins make 90p?

10. How much change is there from £1 after spending 55p?

11. How many surfaces has a triangular pyramid?

12. It is 12·15 pm. What will the time be in 15 minutes?

13. $(9 \times 4) + 8 =$

14. 4·3 kg + 4·5 kg =

15. What is thirty-one less than 51?

How many ways can you make 15, using some or all of these numbers?

10	3	
		7
	5	
2		4

C

1 $\square + 2 = 8$

2 $10 + 6 =$

3 163, 263, 363, $\square$

4 $3 \times 9 =$

5 $50 \div 10 =$

6 $45 - 23 =$

7 $88 + 11 =$

8 $6 + 4 + 6 + 5 =$

9 $5 \times 8 =$

10 $\square - 3 = 4$

11 $14 - 6 =$

12 $28 \div 7 =$

13 −4 −3 −2 $\square$ 0

14 888, 878, 868, $\square$

15 $36 \times 10 =$

Copy and fill in the missing numbers.

```
  5  4  3
-    □  9
---------
  5  1  □
```

D

1 Eighteen minus nine.

2 Is 534 odd or even?

3 Write nine hundred and eighty in numerals.

4 Which of these numbers is divisible by 6? 30, 31, 32

5 Emma had 76 beads. She used 54 to make a necklace. How many beads had she left?

6 Shane drew 8 triangles. How many corners were there altogether?

7 Double 33.

8 What is 1 less 8260?

9 At the cinema Gita buys 2 bags of popcorn at 35p each. How much does this cost her?

10 Estimate the answer to 59 + 59.

11 The book Rashid wanted cost 99p. In the sale all books have 20p off. How much does he have to pay now?

12 Complete this pattern. 60, $\square$, $\square$, 90

13 What is 18 more than 61?

14 Draw a symmetrical cake. Show the line of symmetry.

15 $\frac{1}{10}$ of 10 m =

Exercise 17

A

1. $20 - \square = 5$

2. $94 - 52 =$

3. $3 \times 10 =$

4. $29 + 30 =$

5. $5 + \square = 8$

6. $7 + \square = 15$

7. $429, \square, 431, 432$

8. $3 + 6 + 8 =$

9. $10 - 5 =$

10. $12 \div \square = 2$

11. $42 \div \square = 6$

12. $\square \times 2 = 18$

13. $783, 780, 777, \square$

14. $88 \times 10 =$

15. $\begin{array}{ccccc} & & & & \\ -4 & -3 & \square & -1 & 0 \end{array}$

Copy and complete.

×	5	9	8	1
6				
7				
0				
2				

B

1. Seven plus sixty-two =

2. $753, 748, 743, \square$

3. Put these numbers in order, smallest first.
   555, 515, 551

4. 9 hundreds + 6 units + 8 tens =

5. Three children arrived early for a party.
   16 children arrived at the right time.
   How many children came to the party
   altogether?

6. Eight sets of triplets were born last week.
   How many babies is this?

7. $\frac{1}{10} + \frac{1}{10} + \frac{1}{10} =$

8. Which 6 coins make 86p?

9. Julian used 350 ml from a litre pot of paint.
   How much is left?

10. How much change is there from £1
    after spending 58p?

11. How many edges has a cube?

12. Write the time shown
    on this clock as a digital
    time.

13. $(6 \times 7) + 7 =$

14. $2.7\,m + 3.2\,m =$

15. What is forty-one less than 76?

C

1. $12 - 3 =$

2. $56 - 43 =$

3. $4 \times \boxed{} = 0$

4. $75 + 24 =$

5. $0 + \boxed{} = 4$

6. $5 + 12 =$

7. $979, \boxed{}, 981, 982$

8. $7 + 6 + 5 =$

9. $8 - \boxed{} = 5$

10. $10 \div 2 =$

11. $18 \div \boxed{} = 3$

12. $4 \times 10 =$

13. $-5 \quad -4 \quad \boxed{} \quad -2 \quad -1$

14. $954, 950, 946, \boxed{}$

15. $43 \times 10 =$

How many 1, 2 or 3-digit numbers can you make using these numerals?

	3
5	
	1

D

1. Twenty-four minus eight.

2. Is 229 odd or even?

3. Write six hundred and thirty-one in numerals.

4. Which of these numbers is divisible by 3?
19, 20, 21

5. There were 48 squares of chocolate.
Michael ate 23 of them.
How many were left?

6. 6 teams compete in a 5-a-side competition.
How many players is this altogether?

7. Double 41.

8. What is 1 less than 1462?

9. Bernadette spent 40p on Monday and 36p on Tuesday.
How much did she spend altogether?

10. Estimate the answer to $69 + 69$.

11. Hussain had 40p. He gave half of his money to his sister.
How much had he left?

12. Complete this pattern.
$12, \boxed{}, \boxed{}, 30$

13. What is 13 more than 53?

14. Draw a symmetrical hat.
Show the line of symmetry.

15. $\frac{1}{4}$ of $8\,m =$

Exercise 18

A

1. $11 - 6 =$

2. $96 - 54 =$

3. $7 \times 4 =$

4. $18 + 61 =$

5. $1 + 8 =$

6. $8 + 11 =$

7. 652, ☐, 650, ☐

8. $4 + 8 + 3 + 6 =$

9. $6 - 2 =$

10. $80 \div 8 =$

11. $48 \div 6 =$

12. ☐ $\times 2 = 6$

13. ☐ $-4 \quad -3 \quad -2 \quad -1$

14. 481, 485, 489, ☐

15. $10 \times 25 =$

How many triangles can you find in this shape?

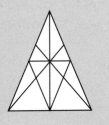

B

1. What is the sum of four and forty-six?

2. 643, 637, 631, ☐

3. 7 units + 8 hundreds + 9 tens =

4. Put these numbers in order, smallest first.
313, 33, 331

5. There were 65 fish swimming in a pond.
Carol added 4 more.
How many fish are there now?

6. Blank cassettes are sold in packs of 10.
How many packs are needed for 60 cassettes?

7. $\frac{1}{5} + \frac{1}{5} + \frac{1}{5} =$

8. How many cm are left if 35 cm are cut from a metre plank of wood?

9. Which 5 coins make 79p?

10. How much change is there from £1 after spending 61p?

11. How many vertices has a square?

12. Which clock shows 11·45?

   a   b   c

13. $(7 \times 4) - 6 =$

14. $5{\cdot}1\,g + 2{\cdot}8\,g =$ ☐ g

15. What is 26 less than forty-nine?

C

1 $\square - 8 = 7$

2 $34 - 22 =$

3 $\square \times 4 = 24$

4 $56 + 32 =$

5 $0 + 6 =$

6 $9 + 5 =$

7 874, 872, $\square$, 868

8 $8 + 3 + 2 + 4 =$

9 $9 - 1 =$

10 $40 \div 8 =$

11 $24 \div \square = 3$

12 $2 \times \square = 4$

13 $-5 \quad -4 \quad -3 \quad -2 \quad \square$

14 127, 131, $\square$, 139

15 $10 \times 59 =$

How many ways are there of showing $\frac{1}{3}$ this shape?

D

1 Twenty-six minus seven.

2 Is 772 odd or even?

3 Write seven hundred and fifty-four in numerals.

4 Which of these numbers is divisible by 4? 35, 36, 37

5 There were 68 buttons in a box. Sarah used 12 when making her coat. How many buttons were left?

6 At the party there were 6 plates on the table. Each plate held 3 cakes. How many cakes were there altogether?

7 Double 24.

8 What is 1 less than 2876?

9 Sue travelled on 2 buses. The first fare cost 37p and the second 25p. How much did it cost her altogether?

10 Estimate the answer to $99 + 99$.

11 Harry buys a newspaper costing 38p. How much change from 60p does he get?

12 Complete this pattern. 15, $\square$, $\square$, 24

13 What is 19 more than 20?

14 Draw a symmetrical apple. Show the line of symmetry.

15 $\frac{1}{2}$ of 10 m =

Exercise 19

(A)

1. $20 - 12 =$

2. $85 - 32 =$

3. $4 \times 1 =$

4. $32 + 45 =$

5. $3 + \square = 3$

6. $3 + \square = 11$

7. $730, 720, 710, \square$

8. $1 + 9 + 4 =$

9. $7 - 0 =$

10. $40 \div 10 =$

11. $36 \div 9 =$

12. $\square \times 7 = 70$

13. $897, \square, 903, 906$

14. $-6 \quad \square \quad -4 \quad -3 \quad -2$

15. $66 \times 10 =$

How many ways can you make 20, using some or all of these numbers?

$$2 \quad 4 \quad 6 \quad 5 \quad 9 \quad 14$$

(B)

1. Seven add fifty-four.

2. $903, 894, 885, \square$

3. 8 tens + 6 units + 8 hundreds + 2 units =

4. Put these numbers in order, smallest first.
484, 444, 448

5. Juginder has 97 marbles. He wins 2 more in a game.
How many does he have now?

6. If there are 4 cakes in a packet, how many packets would you get from 32 cakes?

7. $\frac{1}{10} + \frac{1}{10} + \frac{1}{10} + \frac{1}{10} =$

8. Meera uses 550 grams of flour from a 1 kg packet.
How much flour is still in the packet?

9. Which 6 coins make 69p?

10. How much change from £1 do I get after spending 57p?

11. How many right angles has a circle?

12. Write the time shown on this clock as a digital time.

13. $(3 \times 9) + 8 =$

14. $5{\cdot}5 \text{ kg} + 2{\cdot}4 \text{ kg} = \square \text{ kg}$

15. What is thirty-two less than fifty-nine?

C

1. $15 - 10 =$

2. $77 - 56 =$

3. $\boxed{} \times 10 = 40$

4. $86 + 13 =$

5. $\boxed{} + \boxed{} = 6$

6. $14 + 5 =$

7. 528, 529, $\boxed{}$, $\boxed{}$

8. $6 + 9 + 1 + 7 =$

9. $5 - \boxed{} = 1$

10. $6 - \boxed{} = 2$

11. $27 \div 3 =$

12. $8 \times 2 =$

13.
```
 ┼────┼────┼────┼────┼
-6   -5   -4   □    -2
```

14. 552, 550, $\boxed{}$, 546

15. $10 \times 85 =$

How many 1, 2 or 3-digit numbers can you make using these numerals?

7	2
	1

D

1. Thirty minus nine.

2. Is 131 odd or even?

3. Write two hundred and five in numerals.

4. Which of these numbers is divisible by 6? 23, 24, 25

5. A fruit seller had a box of 96 apples. At the end of the day there were 15 left. How many apples had she sold?

6. Four trains arrive at the station every hour. How many trains will have arrived at the station after 7 hours?

7. Double 24.

8. What is 1 less than 5244?

9. Ice-creams cost 42p each. Troy buys one for himself and one for his friend. How much does this cost him?

10. Estimate the answer to $39 + 39$.

11. Shane had 56p. He dropped 15p on the way to the shop. How much had he left to spend?

12. Complete this pattern. 12, $\boxed{}$, $\boxed{}$, 21

13. What is 12 more than 87?

14. Draw a symmetrical fork. Show the line of symmetry.

15. $\frac{1}{4}$ of 12 m =

Exercise 20

A

1. $11 - \square = 7$

2. $43 - 21 =$

3. $5 \times 6 =$

4. $16 + 21 =$

5. $\square + 1 = 8$

6. $12 + \square = 19$

7. $\square$, 298, 296, 294

8. $3 + 7 + 8 + 3 =$

9. $4 - 2 =$

10. $45 \div 5 =$

11. $6 \div 6 =$

12. $5 \times 1 =$

13. 944, 940, 936, $\square$

14. $10 \times 52 =$

14. $\square$ −5 −4 −3 −2

Copy and complete.

×	1	10	9	4
6				
2				
5				
3				

B

1. What is the sum of nine and eighty-five?

2. 652, 644, 636, $\square$

3. 3 units + 4 tens + 2 hundreds + 4 tens =

4. Put these numbers in order, smallest first.
    717, 272, 227

5. There are 93 members of a choir.
    Seven more people join.
    How many members are in the choir now?

6. How many millilitres are left in a litre carton
    of juice, if Tony drinks 400 millilitres?

7. $\frac{1}{3} + \frac{2}{3} =$

8. How many tricycles can be made with
    18 wheels?

9. Which 5 coins make 66p?

10. How much change is there from £1
    after spending 51p?

11. How many surfaces has a cuboid?

12. The time is 10·45. What will the time be
    in a quarter of an hour?

13. $(8 \times 10) + 7 =$

14. $7·6\,m + 2·2\,m = \square\ m$

15. What is sixteen less than thirty-eight?

C

1. $16 - 7 =$

2. $76 - 42 =$

3. $\square \times 6 = 0$

4. $94 + 5 =$

5. $1 + 9 =$

6. $4 + 10 =$

7. 381, 380, $\square$, 378

8. $7 + 8 + 9 + 2 =$

9. $10 - 6 =$

10. $45 \div \square = 5$

11. $20 \div \square = 4$

12. $10 \times \square = 50$

13. 621, 619, $\square$, 615

14. $27 \times 10 =$

15. $\;$ −6 $\quad$ −5 $\quad\square\quad$ −3 $\quad$ −2

How many ways are there of showing $\frac{1}{5}$ this shape?

D

1. Twenty-seven minus nine.

2. Is 350 odd or even?

3. Write eight hundred and sixty in numerals.

4. Which of these numbers is divisible by 4?
    38, 39, 40

5. There are 88 children in year 4.
    23 go home for dinner.
    How many are still at school?

6. Jason had 9 pairs of shoes mended.
    How many shoes was this altogether?

7. Double 32.

8. What is 1 less than 4567?

9. Kirsty bought a comic for 35p and
    a chocolate bar for 27p.
    How much did she spend altogether?

10. Estimate the answer to $89 + 89$.

11. Kevin had 72p. He gave 31p to his brother.
    How much had he left?

12. Complete this pattern.
    24, $\square$, $\square$, 33

13. What is 14 more than 75?

14. Draw a symmetrical pair of sunglasses.
    Show the line of symmetry.

15. $\frac{1}{5}$ of 15 m

Exercise 21

A

1. $15 \div \square = 5$

2. $6 + 6 + 3 + 1 =$

3. $6 + 4 =$

4. $\square \times 5 = 40$

5. $12 - 8 =$

6. $\square \times 6 = 36$

7. $87 - 63 =$

8. $35 + 23 =$

9. $134, \square, 130, 128$

10. $8 - 8 =$

11. $7 + 10 =$

12. $8 \div 4 =$

13. $\square, 159, 162, 165$

14. $10 \times 39 =$

15. $-9 \quad -8 \quad \square \quad -6 \quad -5$

How many squares can you find in this shape?

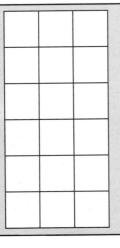

B

1. Twenty-five add forty-three =

2. $296, 305, \square, \square$

3. 4 thousands + 2 hundreds + 6 tens + 4 units =

4. Put these numbers in order, smallest first.
565, 655, 665, 556

5. 23 penguins are standing in a line.
They are joined by 9 more.
How many penguins are there altogether?

6. Yoghurts come in packs of 4. How many packs are made from 40 yoghurts?

7. $2\frac{1}{2} + 1\frac{1}{2} =$

8. How many cm in half a metre?

9. 2 multiplied by itself.

10. How much change is there from a £1 after spending 49p?

11. How many right angles has an exercise book?

12. Write the time shown on this clock as a digital time.

13. $5 \square 6 = 30$

14. Sunil buys an apple for 25p and an orange for 20p.
How much change does he get from £1?

15. $(5 \times 4) - 3 =$

C

1. $24 \div \boxed{} = 3$

2. $5 + 3 + 2 =$

3. $8 + 2 =$

4. $1 \times \boxed{} = 2$

5. $20 - 16 =$

6. $7 \times 6 =$

7. $35 - 24 =$

8. $74 + 13 =$

9. $464, 466, 468, \boxed{}$

10. $\boxed{} - 7 = 3$

11. $9 + 7 =$

12. $18 \div 2 =$

13. $304, 314, \boxed{}, 334$

14. $-8 \quad -7 \quad -6 \quad \boxed{} \quad -4$

15. $10 \times 67 =$

Copy and fill in the missing numbers.

$$\begin{array}{r} \boxed{}\ 3\ 4 \\ \times \qquad 3 \\ \hline 2\ 5\ \boxed{}\ 2 \end{array}$$

D

1. Forty-five minus twenty-two =

2. Is 2 less than 9 odd or even?

3. Which of these numbers is divisible by 3?
   18, 19, 20

4. A paper girl had 78 papers to deliver.
   By 4 o'clock, she has delivered 35.
   How many has she left to deliver?

5. A class was told to get into groups of 4.
   They made 8 groups.
   How many children are in the class?

6. What is $\frac{1}{2}$ of 150?

7. Double 19.

8. What is 3 less than 2972?

9. Lucy has 19p. In her pocket she finds 63p.
   How much has she altogether?

10. Dermot gets 65p from his dad.
    He then gives his sister 28p.
    How much has he left?

11. Estimate the answer to 46 + 23.

12. The film starts at 2·30 pm and lasts
    for $1\frac{1}{2}$ hours.
    What time does it finish?

13. How many boxes of half a dozen eggs
    do I need to make 33 boiled eggs?

14. Estimate how long it takes for an electric
    kettle to boil.
    30 sec, 3 min or 30 min?

15. On Tuesday the temperature is −1°C and on
    Wednesday it is 3°C.
    By how much has the temperature risen?

Exercise 22

A

1. $12 \div \square = 3$

2. $2 + 7 + 4 + 9 =$

3. $\square + 4 = 8$

4. $2 \times 3 =$

5. $14 - \square = 6$

6. $\square \times 9 = 36$

7. $89 - 55 =$

8. $52 + 32 =$

9. 978, $\square$, $\square$, 981

10. $6 - 6 =$

11. $6 + 7 =$

12. $60 \div 6 =$

13. $\square$ −6 −5 −4 −3

14. 583, $\square$, 587, 589

15. $91 \times 10 =$

How many ways can you make 24, using some or all of these numbers?

3 8
12 6
2 5

B

1. Thirty-two plus fifty-four =

2. 793, 773, $\square$, $\square$

3. 2 thousands + 4 tens + 3 units =

4. Put these numbers in order, smallest first.
529, 592, 295, 259

5. Jane has a collection of 36 football programmes. Her uncle gives her 5 more. How many does she have now?

6. Fruit pies come in boxes of 6. How many boxes have I opened if I have 54 pies?

7. $1\frac{1}{4} + 1\frac{1}{2} =$

8. How many grams in $\frac{1}{4}$ kg?

9. 1 multiplied by itself =

10. How much change is there from £1 after spending 47p?

11. How many edges has a photograph?

12. Write the time shown on this clock as a digital time.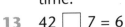

13. $42 \square 7 = 6$

14. Judy buys a drink for 35p and a bar of chocolate for 20p.
How much change does she get from £1?

15. $(9 \times 5) - 8 =$

C

1. $30 \div 5 =$

2. $4 + 2 + 1 =$

3. $5 + 5 =$

4. $\square \times 2 = 8$

5. $11 - 11 =$

6. $5 \times 3 =$

7. $57 - 25 =$

8. $93 + 5 =$

9. 641, $\square$, $\square$, 638

10. $9 - 9 =$

11. $2 + 9 =$

12. $20 \div \square = 5$

13. 741, 746, $\square$, 756

14. -11 $\square$ -9 -8 -7

15. $70 \times 10 =$

How many 1, 2 or 3-digit numbers can you make using these numerals?

8
5
6

D

1. Sixty-seven minus fifty-two =

2. Is 2 less than 18 odd or even?

3. Which of these numbers is divisible by 5?
28, 29, 30

4. There are 52 playing cards in a pack.
Steven deals 7 to Michelle.
How many are left?

5. James lays the tea table with cups, saucers and plates for 8 people.
How many pieces of crockery does he need?

6. What is $\frac{1}{4}$ of 80?

7. Double 26.

8. What is 3 less than 4927?

9. Edward bought a card for 56p and a stamp for 26p.
How much did he spend?

10. Marco had 76p. He bought a sausage roll for 38p.
How much had he left?

11. Estimate the answer to $32 + 49$.

12. Simon gets on the train at $\frac{1}{4}$ past 1.
His journey is for $1\frac{1}{4}$ hours.
What time does he get off the train?

13. Balloons come in bags of 5. How many bags must Kate buy if she needs 43 balloons?

14. Estimate how long it takes to boil an egg.
40 sec, 4 min or 40 min?

15. In January the average temperature is $-2°C$.
In March the average temperature is $5°C$.
How many degrees higher is the average temperature in March?

Exercise 23

A

1. $24 \div \boxed{} = 8$

2. $7 + 3 + 5 + 7 =$

3. $3 + 0 =$

4. $7 \times 5 =$

5. $\boxed{} - 9 = 5$

6. $\boxed{} \times 2 = 6$

7. $38 - 14 =$

8. $37 + 51 =$

9. $835, 837, 839, \boxed{}$

10. $\boxed{} - 2 = 3$

11. $8 + 6 =$

12. $25 \div 5 =$

13. $\boxed{}, 426, 423, 420$

14. $10 \times 28 =$

15. $-13 \quad -12 \quad -11 \quad \boxed{} \quad -9$

Copy and complete.

×	11	4	3	6
9				
1				
5				
7				

B

1. What is the sum of 61 and 18?

2. $260, 245, \boxed{}, \boxed{}$

3. 5 thousands + 2 hundreds + 6 units =

4. Put these numbers in order, smallest first.
   329, 293, 239, 292

5. 48 children are swimming in a pool.
   6 more jump in.
   How many children are in the pool altogether?

6. There are 3 pens in a packet.
   How many packets are needed for 30 pens?

7. $2\frac{1}{3} + 1\frac{1}{3} =$

8. How many ml in $\frac{1}{4}$ litre?

9. 5 multiplied by itself =

10. How much change is there from £1 after spending 38p?

11. How many surfaces has a can of baked beans?

12. Write the time shown on this clock as a digital time.

13. $50 \boxed{} 10 = 5$

14. Simon buys a pencil for 30p and a rubber for 30p.
    How much change does he get from £1?

15. $(5 \times 8) - 11 =$

C

1   $18 \div \square = 6$

2   $3 + 9 + 9 =$

3   $\square + 4 = 7$

4   $\square \times 4 = 40$

5   $20 - 17 =$

6   $6 \times 8 =$

7   $64 - 31 =$

8   $67 + 22 =$

9   $746, 744, \square, 740$

10 $10 - 8 =$

11 $8 + 10 =$

12 $80 \div 10 =$

13 $-12 \quad -11 \quad -10 \quad \square \quad -8$

14 $451, \square, 461, 466$

15 $10 \times 68 =$

How many ways
are there of
showing $\frac{1}{10}$ this
shape?

D

1   Eighty-nine minus forty-two =

2   Is 2 less than 20 odd or even?

3   Which of these numbers is divisible by 10?
    35, 40, 45

4   Terry has 57 football magazines. He lends 22
    to Glen.
    How many has he left?

5   There are 7 donkeys on the beach. How
    many donkeys' legs are there altogether?

6   What is $\frac{1}{2}$ of 90?

7   Double 27.

8   What is 3 less than 5261?

9   Tina buys 2 cans of drink. One costs 32p
    and the other costs 35p.
    How much had she spent altogether?

10 Rocco had 96p. He bought a programme
    for 60p. How much has he left?

11 Estimate the answer to 43 + 28.

12 Vanessa visited her friend in hospital. She
    arrived at 2·15 pm and stayed for $1\frac{1}{2}$ hours.
    At what time did she leave?

13 Oranges come in bags of 10. How many
    bags does Joseph have to buy if he wants
    56 oranges?

14 Estimate the height of the classroom door.
    1 m, 2·5 m or 5 m?

15 Ann owes her mum £2. She gets £5 from
    her aunt and pays her mum back.
    How much money has she left?

Exercise 24

A

1. $32 \div 4 =$

2. $5 + 6 + 6 + 8 =$

3. $5 + 4 =$

4. $7 \times 10 =$

5. $18 - \boxed{} = 3$

6. $\boxed{} \times 6 = 24$

7. $97 - 55 =$

8. $38 + 41 =$

9. $559, \boxed{}, \boxed{}, 562$

10. $3 - 2 =$

11. $7 + 7 =$

12. $40 \div \boxed{} = 5$

13. $278, \boxed{}, 284, 287$

14. $-15 \quad -14 \quad -13 \quad \boxed{} \quad -11$

15. $10 \times 47 =$

How many triangles can you find in this shape?

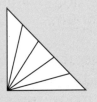

B

1. How much is 23 and 76 altogether?

2. $610, 625, \boxed{}, \boxed{}$

3. 8 thousands + 1 hundreds + 3 tens + 8 units =

4. Put these numbers in order, smallest first.
   999, 919, 991, 195

5. 58 people are staying in a hotel.
   9 more people book in.
   How many guests are there altogether?

6. An insect has 6 legs. How many insects are there if Philip has counted 30 legs?

7. $2\frac{1}{5} + 3\frac{2}{5} =$

8. How many cm in $\frac{1}{5}$ m?

9. 10 multiplied by itself =

10. How much change is there from £1 after spending 42p?

11. How many faces has a lunch box?

12. Write the time shown on this clock as a digital time.

13. $4 \boxed{} 7 = 28$

14. Finbar spends 28p on a drink and 22p on crisps.
    How much change does he get from £1?

15. $(6 \times 8) - 12 =$

C

1. $30 \div \square = 6$

2. $2 + 6 + 8 + 2 =$

3. $3 + 6 =$

4. $\square \times 10 = 90$

5. $512 - 9 =$

6. $3 \times 7 =$

7. $48 - 26 =$

8. $87 + 12 =$

9. $\square$, 264, 265, 266

10. $\square - 4 = 3$

11. $8 + \square = 12$

12. $20 \div 5 =$

13. 821, 827, 833, $\square$

14. $8 \times 10 =$

15. $-14 \ \square \ -12 \ -11 \ -10$

Copy and fill in the missing numbers.

$$5\overline{)6\ 9\ \square} \quad 1\ \square\ 9$$

D

1. Ninety-eight minus thirty-one =

2. Is 2 less than 37 odd or even?

3. Which of these numbers is divisible by 6? 54, 55, 56

4. 84 children go on a camping holiday. 41 have camped before. How many children are camping for the first time?

5. There are 9 girls dancing. How many shoes on the dance floor?

6. What is $\frac{1}{4}$ of 100?

7. Double 35.

8. What is 4 less than 4962?

9. Jake bought a birthday card for 53p and wrapping paper for 25p. How much did he spend altogether?

10. Lily had 96p. She bought a balloon for 35p. How much had she left?

11. Estimate the answer to $48 + 38$.

12. Charlotte's favourite TV programme is 1 hour long. If it finishes at 6·15 pm, when did it start?

13. Tea-cakes come in packs of 6. How many packs are needed for 22 children?

14. Estimate the weight of a banana. 5 g, 50 g or 500 g?

15. Sue owes Helen £1. She gets £2 pocket money and pays Helen back. How much has she left?

Exercise 25

(A)

1. $3 \div 3 =$

2. $6 + 5 + 7 + 5 =$

3. $7 + 0 =$

4. $2 \times 1 =$

5. $20 - 8 =$

6. $\boxed{} \times 3 = 9$

7. $84 - 53 =$

8. $48 + 11 =$

9. $348, 349, \boxed{}, \boxed{}$

10. $2 - 0 =$

11. $9 + 4 =$

12. $16 \div 8 =$

13. $-16 \quad -15 \quad \boxed{} \quad -13 \quad -12$

14. $643, \boxed{}, 637, 634$

15. $16 \times 10 =$

How many ways can you make 37, using some or all of these numbers?

11   6
        8
  14
4   9

(B)

1. What is the total of forty-three and fifty-five?

2. $710, 690, \boxed{}, \boxed{}$

3. 3 thousands + five hundred + 1 ten =

4. Put these numbers in order, smallest first.
414, 441, 404, 440

5. Ann had 67 marbles. She won 8 more in a game.
How many marbles does she have now?

6. 4 plants are grown in a pot. How many pots are there, if there are 36 plants?

7. $2\frac{1}{4} + 1\frac{1}{4} + 3\frac{1}{4} =$

8. How many grams are there in $\frac{1}{4}$ kg?

9. 6 multiplied by itself =

10. How much change is there from £1 after spending 35p?

11. How many surfaces has a cereal box?

12. Write the time shown on this clock as a digital time.

13. $32 \boxed{} 8 = 4$

14. Frederick spends 35p on a notebook and 50p on coloured pencils.
How much change does he get from £1?

15. $(9 \times 6) - 11 =$

C

1. $\square \times 5 = 50$

2. $36 - 15 =$

3. $8 \div \square = 4$

4. $70 \times 7 =$

5. $4 + 4 + 7 + 5 =$

6. $\square \times 6 = 30$

7. $2 + \square = 2$

8. $7 + 8 =$

9. $9 - \square = 1$

10. $\square - 9 = 7$

11. $85 + 13 =$

12. $131, \boxed{}, \boxed{}, 128$

13. $978, 984, \boxed{}, 996$

14. $-19 \quad -18 \quad -17 \quad -16 \quad \boxed{}$

15. $76 \times 10 =$

How many 1, 2 or 3-digit numbers can you make using these numerals?

	9
7	
	6

D

1. Fifty-nine minus thirty-six =

2. Is 2 less than 100 odd or even?

3. Which of these numbers is divisible by 2?
   19, 20, 21

4. The café has 85 glasses.
   35 have been used.
   How many clean glasses are left?

5. There are 3 daffodils in each pot.
   There are 9 pots in the greenhouse.
   How many daffodils are there altogether?

6. What is $\frac{1}{2}$ of 88?

7. Double 24.

8. What is 4 less than 3651?

9. Cara paid 34p for sweets and 27p for a packet of tissues.
   How much did she spend?

10. Myra had 56p. She put 30p in a drawer.
    How much did she leave out?

11. Estimate the answer to $49 + 29$.

12. Maureen went to sleep at 10 o'clock.
    She woke at 7 o'clock the next morning.
    How long did she sleep?

13. Wafer biscuits come in packs of 5.
    How many packs must Sandy buy for 27 people?

14. Estimate how tall your teacher is.

15. John owes his Dad £3. He wins £5 in a raffle.
    How much has he left after he has paid his Dad back?

Exercise 26

A

1. $10 \times 8 =$

2. $99 - 54 =$

3. $21 \div 3 =$

4. $30 \div 5 =$

5. $5 + 7 + 8 + 6 =$

6. $10 \times \boxed{} = 30$

7. $3 + 5 =$

8. $10 + 9 =$

9. $5 - 0 =$

10. $11 - 7 =$

11. $42 + 53 =$

12. 445, 444, 443, $\boxed{}$

13. 398, $\boxed{}$, 404, 407

14. $10 \times 96 =$

15. $-18 \quad \boxed{} \quad -16 \;-15 \;-14$

Copy and complete.

×	6	3	9	12
2				
7				
8				
4				

B

1. Thirty-four add sixty-five =

2. 796, 804, $\boxed{}$, $\boxed{}$

3. 3 hundreds + 4 tens + 1 thousand + 6 units =

4. Put these numbers in order, smallest first.
   553, 335, 535, 353

5. There are 5 teams of 11 playing football in a tournament. Another team joins them. How many children are now playing in the tournament?

6. A flower has 6 petals. How many flowers will there be if there are 18 petals?

7. $2\frac{1}{2} + 2\frac{1}{4} + 1\frac{1}{4} =$

8. How many cm in $\frac{1}{5}$ m?

9. 4 multiplied by itself =

10. How much change is there from £1 after spending 26p?

11. How many edges has a tin can?

12. Write the time shown on this clock as a digital time.

13. $24 \boxed{} 6 = 4$

14. Amy buys a cake for 23p and a drink for 37p.
    How much change does she get from £1?

15. $(36 \div 6) + 4 =$

C

1. $8 \times \boxed{} = 16$

2. $54 - 32 =$

3. $24 \div \boxed{} = 6$

4. $14 \div \boxed{} = 2$

5. $7 + 9 + 6 =$

6. $9 \times 6 =$

7. $2 + 7 =$

8. $\boxed{} + 5 = 13$

9. $4 - 4 =$

10. $20 - \boxed{} = 2$

11. $68 + 31 =$

12. $987, 988, \boxed{}, \boxed{}$

13. $-20 \boxed{} -18 \ -17 \ -16$

14. $121, 221, 321, \boxed{}$

15. $38 \times 10 =$

How many ways are there of showing $\frac{1}{4}$ this shape?

D

1. Forty-seven minus twenty-five =

2. Is 10 less than 37 odd or even?

3. Which of these numbers is divisible by 4? 39, 40, 41

4. Sally has collected 49 football cards. She gives 14 to her brother. How many has she left?

5. There are 8 sausages in a pack. How many sausages are in 5 packs?

6. What is $\frac{1}{4}$ of 40?

7. Double 26.

8. What is 4 less than 2721?

9. Leon bought a notepad for 39p and a pencil for 15p. How much did he spend?

10. Trevor had 98p. He bought biscuits for his dog which cost 60p. How much had he left?

11. Estimate the answer to 51 − 29.

12. It takes Winston $2\frac{1}{2}$ hours to get to his grandmother's house. If he leaves at 2·45 pm, when does he arrive?

13. How many boxes of 10 choc-ices does Mrs Barker have to buy for her class of 27 children?

14. Estimate the length of a school paintbrush.

15. The temperature was −2°C. It has dropped another 2 degrees. What is the temperature now?

Exercise 27

A

1. $4 \times 5 =$

2. $74 - 22 =$

3. $30 \div \square = 5$

4. $90 \div 10 =$

5. $2 + 8 + 9 + 4 =$

6. $\square \times 4 = 28$

7. $4 + \square = 10$

8. $11 + 5 =$

9. $10 - 9 =$

10. $17 - 6 =$

11. $63 + 25 =$

12. $620, \boxed{}, 618, 617$

13. $-22 \quad -21 \quad \boxed{} \quad -19 \quad -18$

14. $711, 715, 719, \boxed{}$

15. $10 \times 81 =$

How many rectangles can you find in this shape?

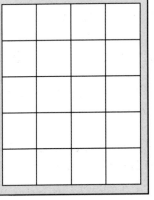

B

1. Seventy-nine plus twenty =

2. $879, 871, \boxed{}, \boxed{}$

3. 2 units + 2 thousands + 4 tens =

4. Put these numbers in order, smallest first.
   121, 212, 211, 112

5. 44 trees are growing in a wood.
   33 trees are planted beside them.
   How many trees are there altogether?

6. A trio is a group of three people.
   How many trios can be formed from 15 people?

7. $3\frac{1}{10} + 2\frac{2}{10} =$

8. How many cm in $\frac{1}{10}$ m?

9. 5 multiplied by itself =

10. How much change is there from £1 after spending 31p?

11. How many right angles does a door have?

12. Write the time shown on this clock as a digital time.

13. $8 \square 4 = 32$

14. Tim buys a comic for 60p and a chew for 7p.
    How much change does he get from £1?

15. $(50 \div 5) - 8 =$

C

1 $\Box \times 5 = 35$

2 $59 - 36 =$

3 $21 \div \Box = 7$

4 $4 \div 2 =$

5 $6 + 8 + 1 + 1 =$

6 $2 \times 4 =$

7 $2 + 5 =$

8 $13 + 6 =$

9 $\Box - 2 = 6$

10 $13 - 8 =$

11 $95 + 14 =$

12 848, 849, $\boxed{}$, 851

13 550, 555, $\boxed{}$, 565

14 $\boxed{}$ —23 —22 —21 —20

15 $46 \times 10 =$

Copy and fill in the missing numbers.

$$6 \overline{)7\ \Box\ 4} = 1\ \Box\ 9$$

D

1 Sixty-five minus thirty-one =

2 Is 10 less than 48 odd or even?

3 Which of these numbers is divisible by 4?
   36, 37, 38

4 There are 75 spaces in the car park.
   32 are filled.
   How many spaces are empty?

5 There are 6 candles in a box.
   In the cupboard there are 7 boxes.
   How many candles is this?

6 What is $\frac{1}{4}$ of 44?

7 Double 36.

8 What is 4 less than 6231?

9 Tolu saved 49p from her pocket money
   for two weeks.
   How much did she save altogether?

10 Jonathan had 80p. He spent 65p
    at the fun fair.
    How much had he left?

11 Estimate the answer to 62 – 26.

12 Wendy's dance lesson is $1\frac{1}{4}$ hours long.
    If it finishes at 5 o'clock, when does it start?

13 23 children are coming to Ranjit's party.
    Cans of cola come in packs of 4.
    How many packs must Ranjit's dad buy?

14 Estimate how many mugs it would take
    to fill a litre container.

15 Chris owes his brother £10. He earns £20
    and pays his brother back.
    How much money has Chris left?

Exercise 28

A

1. $10 \times 9 =$

2. $69 - 48 =$

3. $40 \div \square = 4$

4. $35 \div 5 =$

5. $6 + 3 + 4 + 5 =$

6. $\square \times 4 = 4$

7. $2 + 6 =$

8. $8 + 8 =$

9. $7 - 1 =$

10. $19 - 7 =$

11. $44 - 34 =$

12. 739, $\boxed{}$, 741, 742

13. 436, $\boxed{}$, 428, 424

14. $10 \times 27 =$

15. $-23 \quad -22 \quad -21 \quad -20 \quad \boxed{}$

How many ways can you make 46, using some or all of these numbers?

12	3	
		6
	4	
8	2	

B

1. What is the sum of thirty-two and fifty-seven?

2. 195, 202, $\boxed{}$, $\boxed{}$

3. 3 thousands + 8 units + 8 tens =

4. Put these numbers in order, smallest first.
779, 997, 797, 979

5. There are 26 children in Class 1 and 31 in Class 2.
How many children are in both classes?

6. There are seven people in a netball team. How many teams can be formed from 70 people?

7. $3\frac{2}{5} + 2\frac{2}{5} =$

8. How many grams in $\frac{1}{5}$ of a kilogram?

9. 3 multiplied by itself plus 8 =

10. How much change is there from £1 after spending 28p?

11. How many corners has a square pyramid?

12. Write the time shown on this clock as a digital time.

13. $36 \square 4 = 9$

14. Angela buys 2 bars of chocolate at 28p each.
How much change does she get from £1?

15. $(54 \div 9) + 10 = \square$

C

1. $9 \times 2 =$

2. $93 - 32 =$

3. $54 \div \square = 9$

4. $20 \div 2 =$

5. $4 + 7 + 2 =$

6. $8 \times 4 =$

7. $8 + \square = 9$

8. $7 + 11 =$

9. $\square - 3 = 6$

10. $\square - 10 = 2$

11. $76 + 12 =$

12. $531,\ \square,\ \square,\ 528$

13. $-25\quad -24\quad -23\quad -22\quad \square$

14. $624,\ 630,\ 636,\ \square$

15. $53 \times 10 =$

How many ways are there of showing $\frac{1}{6}$ this shape?

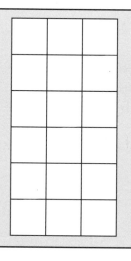

D

1. Seventy-eight minus fourteen =

2. Is 10 less than 39 an odd or even number?

3. Which of these numbers is divisible by 4? 31, 32, 33

4. There are 68 books on the library shelf. The librarian removes 15. How many are left?

5. There are 6 pies in pack. How many pies in 9 packs?

6. What is $\frac{1}{2}$ of 250?

7. Double 43.

8. What is 5 less than 8762?

9. Rory had 57p and Simon had 42p. How much had they got altogether?

10. Natalie had 83p. She paid 59p for a hair slide. How much had she left?

11. Estimate the answer to $72 - 29$.

12. Auntie came to visit for $1\frac{1}{2}$ hours. She arrived at 2·15 pm. When did she leave?

13. The supermarket sells large bags of crisps, each containing 6 packets. How many bags must Mr Jones buy if there are 20 children at the party?

14. Estimate the weight of a 30 cm ruler. 2 g, 20 g or 200 g?

15. The temperature is 1°C. During the night it gets 2 degrees colder. What is the night-time temperature?

Exercise 29

A

1. $2 \times 2 =$

2. $37 - 15 =$

3. $20 \div \square = 5$

4. $12 \div 6 =$

5. $8 + 4 + 3 + 3 =$

6. $6 \times \square = 18$

7. $7 + 3 =$

8. $5 + 15 =$

9. $8 - 0 =$

10. $17 - 8 =$

11. $47 + 22 =$

12. 202, 201, $\square$, $\square$

13. 828, 831, 834, $\square$

14. $10 \times 65 =$

15. $-37 \quad -36 \quad -35 \quad \square \quad -33$

Copy and complete.

×	6	11	10	12
9				
7				
8				
5				

B

1. How much is twenty-six and forty-four altogether?

2. 427, 438, $\square$, $\square$

3. 2 tens + 4 units + 6 thousands =

4. Put these numbers in order, smallest first.
321, 231, 123, 213

5. 21 people are waiting for a train. When it arrives there are already 77 people on it. How many passengers are there altogether?

6. 6 fish can swim in a tank. How many tanks are needed for 42 fish?

7. $3\frac{1}{4} + 2\frac{3}{4} =$

8. How many ml in $\frac{1}{10}$ l?

9. 6 multiplied by itself, plus 4 =

10. How much change is there from £1 after spending £0·19?

11. How many edges has a picture frame?

12. Write the time shown on this clock as a digital time.

13. $6 \square 4 = 24$

14. Geoffrey spends £0·52 on a card and £0·26 on a stamp.
How much change does he get from £1·00?

15. $(42 \div 6) + 7 =$

C

1. $\square \times 1 = 5$

2. $95 - 64 =$

3. $24 \div \square = 4$

4. $5 \div 1 =$

5. $2 + 9 + 6 =$

6. $3 \times 0 =$

7. $5 + \square = 9$

8. $9 + 11 =$

9. $4 - 3 =$

10. $14 - 5 =$

11. $26 + 31 =$

12. 314, 316, 318, $\square$

13. 226, $\square$, 216, 211

14. $\boxed{}$ −41 −40 −39 −38

15. $89 \times 10 =$

How many 1, 2 or 3-digit numbers can you make using these numerals?

$\boxed{\begin{array}{ccc} & & 2 \\ 8 & & \\ & 9 & \end{array}}$

D

1. Ninety-five minus forty-four =

2. Is 20 less than 73 an odd or even number?

3. Which of these numbers is divisible by 5? 54, 55, 56

4. Tara had 59 beads. She used 35 to make a bracelet. How many beads has she left?

5. There are 5 birthday cards in a pack. If I buy 8 packs, how many cards do I have?

6. What is $\frac{1}{3}$ of 60?

7. Double 53.

8. What is 5 less than 8794?

9. Fiona spent 45p on a fair-ride and 45p on some candyfloss. How much did she spend in total?

10. Nancy had 76p. She put 35p in her purse. How much did she leave out?

11. Estimate the answer to 58 − 39.

12. James leaves for school at 8·15 am. It takes him $\frac{1}{2}$ hour to walk to school. At what time does he arrive?

13. How many boxes of 3 candles does Kay have to buy if she needs 29 candles?

14. Estimate how many tablespoons of water you would need to fill a $\frac{1}{2}$ litre container. 3, 33 or 333?

15. Annie has £5. She wants to buy a bag that costs £6. How much must she borrow?

Exercise 30

A

1. $15 - \square = 6$

2. $110, \square, 112, 113$

3. $10 \times 10 =$

4. $4 + 9 + 5 + 2 =$

5. $75 - 42 =$

6. $10 - \square = 0$

7. $36 \div 6 = \square$

8. $2 \div 2 =$

9. $1 + \square = 7$

10. $6 \times 10 =$

11. $54 + 42 =$

12. $10 + 10 =$

13. $935, 945, \square, 965$

14. $10 \times 54 =$

15. $-55 \quad -54 \quad -53 \quad -52 \quad \square$

How many triangles can you find in this shape?

B

1. What is the total of thirty-seven and sixty-three?

2. $672, 660, \square, \square$

3. 2 thousands + 6 hundreds + 2 tens + 1 hundred + 3 units =

4. Put these numbers in order, smallest first.
   443, 334, 343, 434

5. On Monday Roland collected 63 shells on the beach. On Tuesday he found 25 more. How many shells does he have altogether?

6. There are 40 new tyres in a garage. How many cars can have 4 new tyres?

7. $1\frac{2}{5} + 2\frac{1}{5} + 4\frac{2}{5} =$

8. How many cm in $\frac{3}{4}$ m?

9. 10 multiplied by itself, add 7 =

10. How much change is there from £1·00 after spending £0·11?

11. How many vertices has a cube?

12. Write the time shown on this clock as a digital time.

13. $60 \square 6 = 10$

14. Jack buys 2 drinks at £0·25 each and a packet of crisps at £0·32. How much change does he get from £1·00?

15. $(36 \div 4) + 6 =$

C

1. $20 - 19 =$

2. $435, 437, 439, \boxed{}$

3. $7 \times \boxed{} = 14$

4. $6 + 7 + 7 =$

5. $49 - 35 =$

6. $2 - 1 =$

7. $60 \div \boxed{} = 6$

8. $100 \div 10 =$

9. $5 + \boxed{} = 6$

10. $\boxed{} \times 3 = 12$

11. $56 + 33 =$

12. $10 + \boxed{} = 14$

13. $355, 362, 369, \boxed{}$

14. $-78 \quad -77 \quad \boxed{} \quad -75 \quad -74$

15. $29 \times 10 =$

How many ways are there of showing $\frac{1}{6}$ this shape?

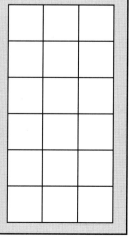

D

1. Eighty-nine minus seventy-eight =

2. Is 20 less than 68 an odd or even number?

3. Which of these numbers is divisible by 6?
   48, 49, 50

4. The video shop had 88 new videos delivered. 26 were already booked.
   How many can go on the shelf?

5. Bananas come in bunches of 3.
   How many bananas on 8 bunches?

6. What is $\frac{1}{3}$ of 90?

7. Double 48.

8. What is 5 less than 9582?

9. Ria was given 35p by her sister and 45p by her brother.
   How much money does she have now?

10. A toy car was priced at 69p. In the sale it had 15p off.
    How much does it cost in the sale?

11. Estimate the answer to $86 - 59$.

12. The concert begins at 7·30 pm and finishes at 8·45 pm.
    How long is the concert?

13. How many books of 4 stamps does Sheila have to buy if she has 38 letters to post?

14. How long it would take your class to say the 2-times table together?
    30 sec, 3 min or 30 min?

15. At 6 am the temperature is −3°C. By 11 am the temperature is 2°C.
    How many degrees has the temperature risen by?